Once "Upon" a Nice Round Belly

By Oriama

Illustrated by TullipStudio

Independently Published

Copyrights 2021 Oriamagic
All rights reserved.

Hardcover ISBN: 978-0-578-31908-7
Paperback ISBN: 979-8-540-43565-9

This is a work of fiction, for as much as the joy of expecting a baby can be defined as a work of fiction. While as in all fiction, the literary perceptions and insights are based upon each and every one of us parents' personal experiences, all names, places and incidents are either products of the author's imagination or are used fictitiously. No reference to any real person is intended or should be inferred.

Creative Concept at text by Oriama
Illustrations by Tullip Studio
Typesetting & format by Enterline Design

To all the rainbows,
the babies . . . and the journey.

Something magical is happening. Mama has a beautiful smile and, would you look at that, she has a nice round belly, too!

Oh! How yummy! Mama is eating a delicious ice cream with strawberries!
Do you like strawberries?
What is your favorite fruit?

Purr... purr...Milo the cat is purring happily curled up on Mama's belly. Is he the surprise Mama and Daddy have been waiting for?

La la la! La di da, la la di da!

Can you hear the music? Is Mama's belly singing? Or is Mama playing music to her belly?

How sweet. Mama and
Daddy are holding hands.
Do you think Mama's belly
is getting **bigger?**

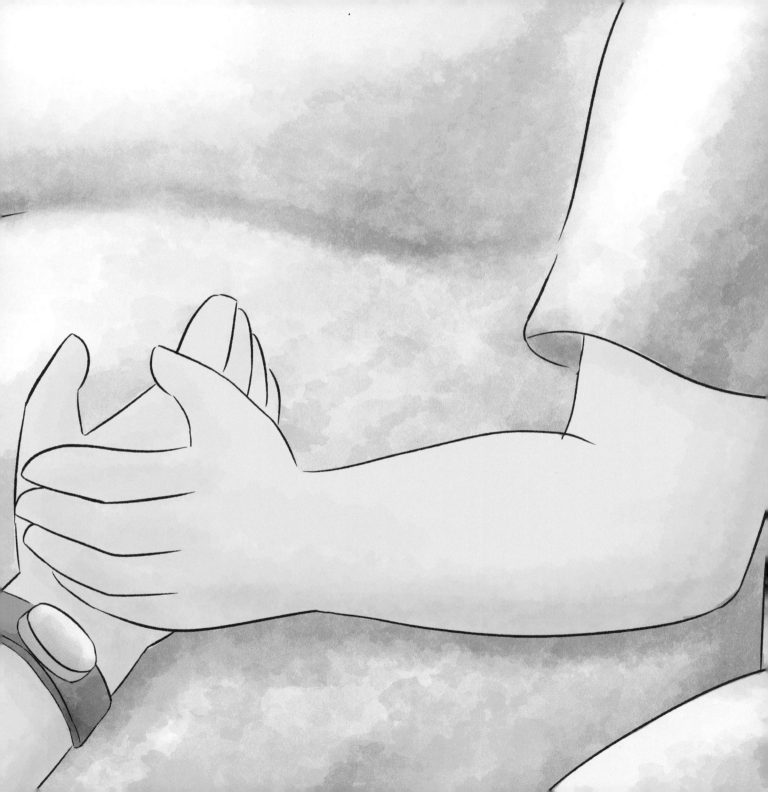

Mama is smiling again.
Is someone tickling her
nice round belly?

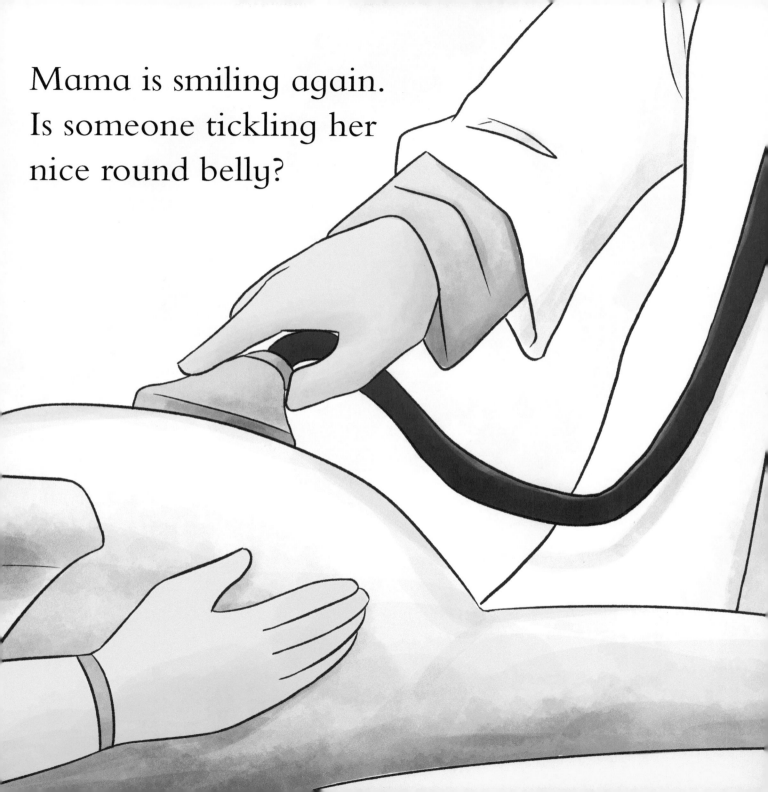

Oh, look at Daddy's face! What is happening? Mama is giggling and Daddy looks so surprised!

Oh, look! There is a baby
in Mama's belly! And what
is the baby doing? Sending
loving kisses to Daddy?

Mama's nice round belly is gone, gone and you are here, finally!

You, dear _____, our precious baby, you are the surprise Mama and Daddy have been waiting for!

About the author:

Oriama is a local Pacific Northwest artist & full-time mother of two rainbow babies. Her pen name, Oriama, is a combination of her children's names, Oriana & Mattia. *Once "Upon" a Nice Round Belly* is the first book of a series dedicated to celebrating motherhood and life.

www.oriamagic.com

Lightning Source UK Ltd.
Milton Keynes UK
UKHW051108131221
395470UK00002B/13